The Wonky Donkey

Words and music by **Craig Smith**

Illustrations by **Katz Cowley**

SCHOLASTIC

AUCKLAND   SYDNEY   NEW YORK   LONDON   TORONTO

MEXICO CITY   NEW DELHI   HONG KONG

I was walking down the road
and I saw ...

a donkey,

Hee Haw)!

And he only had three legs!

He was a
wonky donkey.

I was walking down the road
and I saw a donkey,

Hee Haw!

He only had three legs ...

and one eye!

He was a **winky** wonky donkey.

I was walking down the road
and I saw a donkey,

Hee Haw!

He only had three legs,
one eye ...

and he liked to listen to country music.

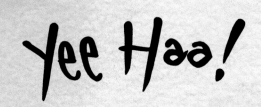

Yee Haa!

He was a **honky-tonky**
winky wonky donkey.

I was walking down the road
and I saw a donkey,

Hee Haw!

He only had three legs,
one eye,
he liked to listen to country music ...

and he was quite tall and slim.

He was
a **lanky**
honky-
tonky
winky
wonky
donkey.

I was walking down the road
and I saw a donkey,

Hee Haw!

He only had three legs,
one eye,
he liked to listen to country music,
he was quite tall and slim ...

and he smelt really, really bad.

He was a **stinky-dinky** lanky honky-tonky winky wonky donkey.

I was walking down the road
and I saw a donkey,

Hee Haw!

He only had three legs,
one eye,
he liked to listen to country music,
he was quite tall and slim,
he smelt really, really bad ...

and that morning he'd got up early
and hadn't had any coffee.

He was a **cranky**
stinky-dinky lanky
honky-tonky
winky wonky donkey.

I was walking down the road
and I saw a donkey,

Hee Haw!

He only had three legs,

one eye,

he liked to listen to country music,

he was quite tall and slim,

he smelt really, really bad,

that morning he'd got up early

and hadn't had any coffee ...

and he was always getting up to mischief.

He was a **hanky-panky** cranky stinky-dinky
lanky honky-tonky winky wonky donkey.

I was walking down the road
and I saw a donkey,

Hee Haw!

He only had three legs,

one eye,

he liked to listen to country music,

he was quite tall and slim,

he smelt really, really bad,

that morning he'd got up early

and hadn't had any coffee,

he was always getting up to mischief ...

but he was quite good looking!

He was a **spunky** hanky-panky cranky
stinky-dinky lanky honky-tonky winky wonky donkey!

I was walking down the road

and I saw a donkey ...

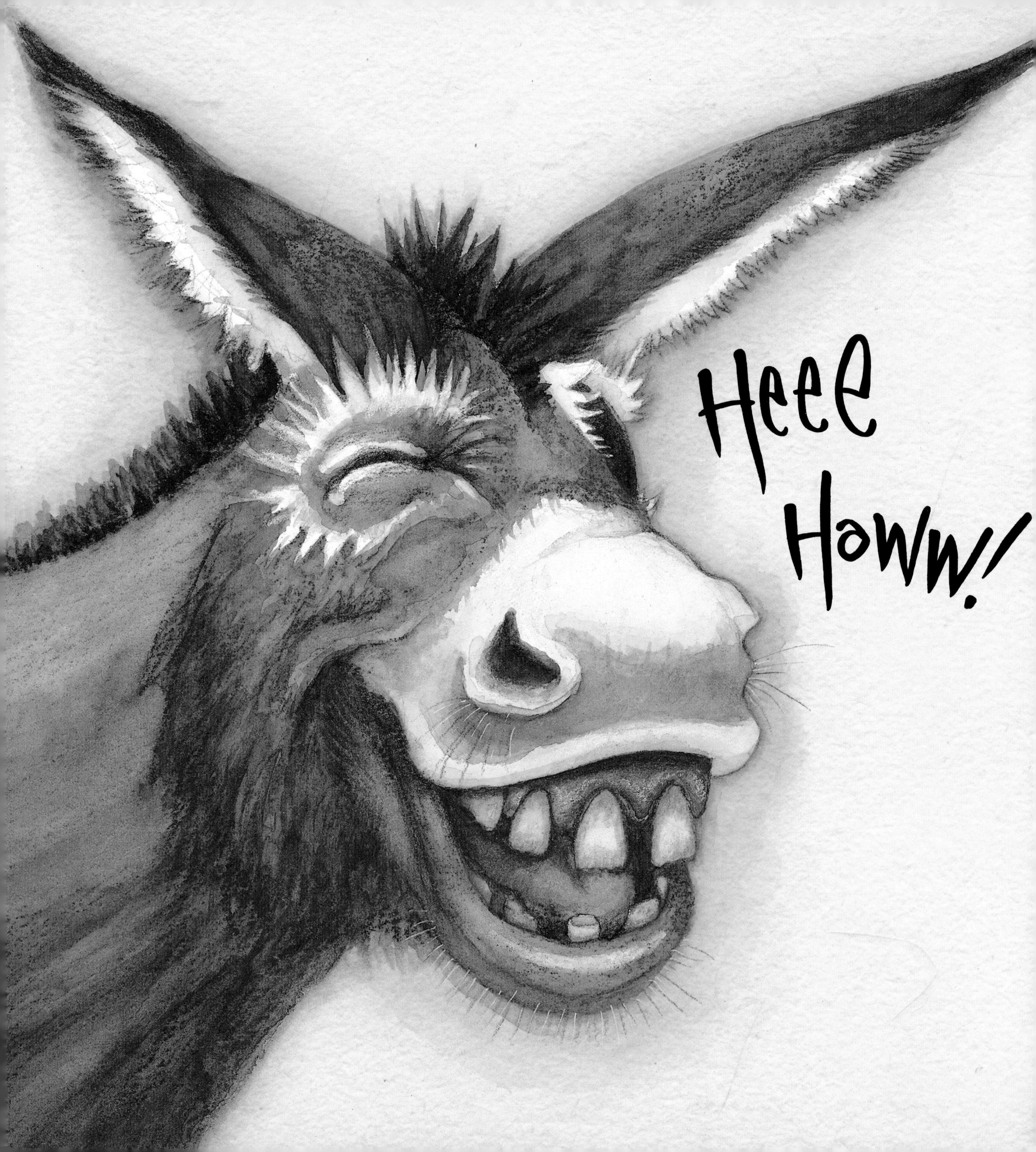
Heee
Howw!